Core Knowledge Language Arts®

Unit 10
Workbook

Skills Strand
KINDERGARTEN

Amplify learning.

Core Knowledge®

Unit 10
Workbook

This workbook contains worksheets that accompany many of the lessons from the *Teacher Guide* for Unit 10. Each worksheet is identified by the lesson number in which it is used. The worksheets in this book do not include written instructions for students because the instructions would have words that are not decodable. Teachers will explain these worksheets to the students orally, using the instructions in the teacher guides. The workbook is a student component, which means each student should have a workbook.

Directions: Have students trace and copy the digraph and words. Students should say the sounds while writing the spellings.

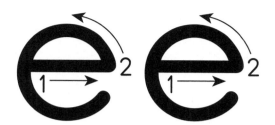

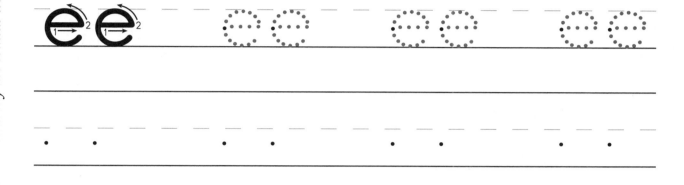

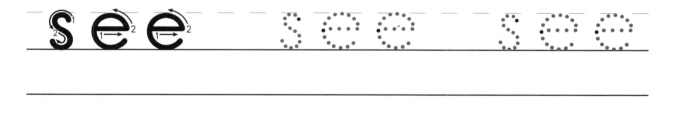

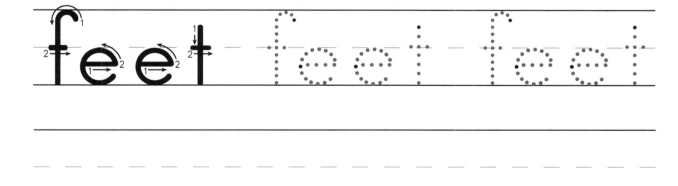

sheep	weeds
f**ee**t	qu**ee**n

_____

\- \- \- \- \- \- \- \- \- \- \- \- \- \- \- \- \-

_____

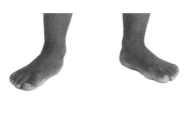

_____

\- \- \- \- \- \- \- \- \- \- \- \- \- \- \- \- \-

_____

Directions: Have students write each word under its matching picture.

pen

Directions: Have students copy the word on the line. Students should illustrate at least one meaning of the word.

feet	**see**ms	**nee**ds

Directions: Have students write each word on the line where it fits best.

1. That kid _____ mad.

2. Dad has socks on his

_____

_____ .

3. Ann _____ ten in cash.

keep	feed	bee

4. Mom was stung by a

_____

_____ .

5. What did Zack _____

his dog?

6. I will _____ my sheep

in a pen.

Dear Family Member,

Have your child read each word and then write it under the matching picture. If necessary, identify the pictures for your child.

1. b**ee**

_____

- - - - - - - - - - - - - - - - -

_____

2. tr**ee**

_____

- - - - - - - - - - - - - - - - -

_____

3. f**ee**t

_____

- - - - - - - - - - - - - - - - -

_____

4. d**ee**r

_____   _____

5. t**ee**th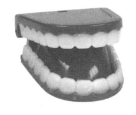

_____   _____

6. sl**ee**p

_____   _____

The Bees

1. <u>What</u> stung **Lee** on his ch**ee**k and f**ee**t?

_____

- -

_____

- -

_____

- -

_____

2. <u>Wh</u>en did Scott get mad?

_____

- -

_____

- -

_____

- -

_____

3. <u>What</u> did Scott tell the bees to sting?

Directions: In the box, have students illustrate a part of the story and then write a caption below.

Dear Family Member,

This is a story your child has read at school. Encourage your child to read the story to you, using his or her finger to point to each word, and then talk about it together. The bolded letters 'ee' are a new spelling your child is learning.

Scott and Lee

This is Scott Gr**ee**n. Scott is ten.

Scott's dad k**ee**ps a pig in a pen.
Scott's mom k**ee**ps thr**ee** hens.
Scott k**ee**ps a sh**ee**p.

L**ee** the Sh**ee**p is Scott's pet.
Scott f**ee**ds L**ee** and rubs him on the back. L**ee** is a sw**ee**t sh**ee**p.

Directions: Have students answer the questions by writing yes or no.

1. Can a tr**ee** sing a song?

_____

2. Is th**ere** a kid in this class with six f**ee**t?

_____

3. <u>Are</u> plants from s**ee**ds?

_____

4. <u>Are</u> the things in a shop fr**ee**?

_____

5. Is th**ere** a kid in this class with thr**ee** hands?

_____

6. Can a b**ee** buzz?

_____

7. Is a sh**ee**p a bug?

_____

- - - - - - - - -

_____

8. <u>Are</u> plums sw**ee**t?

_____

- - - - - - - - -

_____

9. Is grass gr**ee**n?

_____

- - - - - - - - -

_____

10. Can w<u>e</u> munch on rocks?

_____

- - - - - - - - -

_____

11. Can plants s**ee**?

_____

- - - - - - - - -

_____

12. Can a cat sl**ee**p?

_____

- - - - - - - - -

_____

Directions: Have students copy and then write from memory each Tricky Word.

1. _____   _____

2. _____   _____

3. _____   _____

4. _____   _____

5. _____   _____

6. _____   _____

7. _____   _____

Name _____

me	he	We

Directions: Have students write each word on the line where it fits best. Remind students that the first word in a sentence is always capitalized.

1. Seth has a hat that _____

got from his dad.

2. _____ are best pals.

3. I need to sweep the

deck. Will you help _____ ?

she	Which	be

4. If I get in the pond, I will

_____ wet.

5. _____ cup is his?

6. Mom has a dress that

_____ got from a shop.

a_e as in make

Directions: Have students trace and copy the words. Students should say the sounds while writing the spellings.

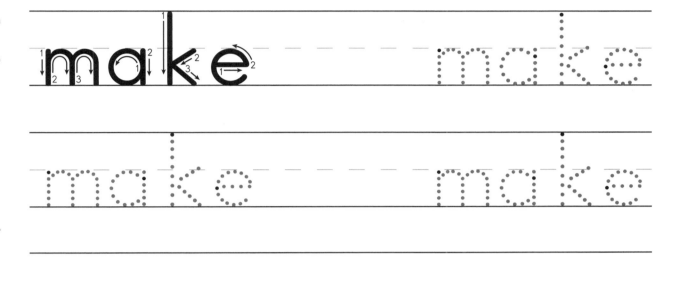

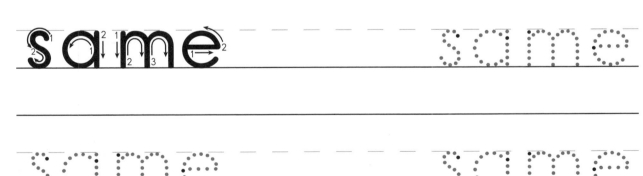

Print the w<u>or</u>d <u>where</u> it fits best.

1. t**a**pe

_____   _____
- - - - - - - - - - - - -   - - - - - - - - - - - - -
_____   _____

2. pl**a**ne

_____   _____
- - - - - - - - - - - - -   - - - - - - - - - - - - -
_____   _____

3. sk**a**te

_____   _____
- - - - - - - - - - - - -   - - - - - - - - - - - - -
_____   _____

Dear Family Member,

This is a story your child has read at school. Encourage your child to read the story to you, and then talk about it together.

Red Ants

Lee the Sheep had a bad week last week. Red ants bit him on his legs and feet.

Scott had to sweep the ants with his hand to get rid of them.

Scott w<u>a</u>s mad at the ants.

"Ants," he s<u>ai</u>d, "L<u>ee</u> is a sw<u>ee</u>t sh<u>ee</u>p. F<u>ee</u>l fr<u>ee</u> to munch on plants and w<u>ee</u>ds, but not on L<u>ee</u>!"

One of the ants said, "W<u>e</u> f<u>ee</u>l bad. W<u>e</u> will not munch on L<u>ee</u>. W<u>e</u> will munch on plants and w<u>ee</u>ds."

Name _____

Dear Family Member,

Have your child read and copy each word under the matching picture. If necessary, identify the pictures for your child.

cake	lake
grapes	cane

_____

- - - - - - - - - - - - - - -

_____

_____

- - - - - - - - - - - - - - -

_____

_____

- - - - - - - - - - - - - - -

_____

_____

- - - - - - - - - - - - - - -

_____

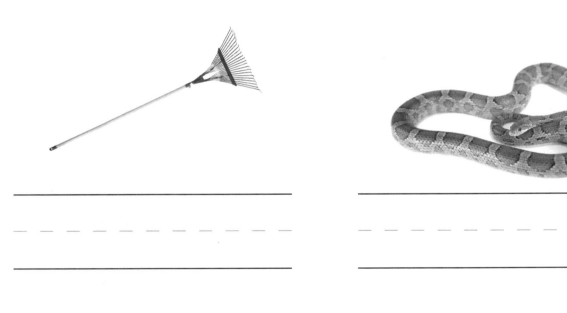

snake   cape

plate   rake

_____
- - - - - - - - - - -
_____

_____
- - - - - - - - - - -
_____

cap **c**a**pe**

man **m**a**ne**

tap **t**a**pe**

plan **pl**a**ne**

rat **r**a**te**

fat **f**a**te**

| pan | p**a**ne |

| mad | m**a**de |

| scrap | scr**a**pe |

| at | **a**te |

| cap | c**a**pe |

| man | m**a**ne |

Fun in the Sand

1. <u>What</u> did the kids m**ake** with the sand?

_____

- -

_____

_____

- -

_____

_____

- -

_____

2. <u>What</u> hit the sand man?

◯ a truck

◯ a ship

◯ a w**a**ve

Directions: Have students reread the story and answer the questions.

3. Did the kids feel sad?

Directions: In the box, have students illustrate a part of the story and write a caption below.

slump

Directions: Have students copy the word on the line. Students should illustrate at least one meaning of the word.

sag

Dear Family Member,

This is a story your child has read at school. Encourage your child to read the story to you, using his or her finger to point word by word, and then talk about it together.

TAKE HOME

The Bees

The red ants left. But then the bees got Lee! The bees stung Lee on his cheek and on his feet.

Scott ran up to help Lee. Then he went and had a chat with the bees.

"B<u>ee</u>s," s<u>ai</u>d Scott, "why sting L<u>ee</u> the Sh<u>ee</u>p? H<u>e</u> is a sw<u>ee</u>t sh<u>ee</u>p."

One b<u>ee</u> s<u>ai</u>d, "B<u>ee</u>s will b<u>e</u> b<u>ee</u>s."

One b<u>ee</u> s<u>ai</u>d, "<u>I</u> must b<u>e</u> m<u>e</u>."

Then Scott got mad. H<u>e</u> s<u>ai</u>d, "Sting the pig. Sting the hens! Sting the cat. Sting the dog. But let L<u>ee</u> b<u>e</u>!" And the b<u>ee</u>s let L<u>ee</u> be.

1. cake   cane

_____

- - - - - - - - - - - - - - - - - -

_____

2. we   weep

_____

- - - - - - - - - - - - - - - - - -

_____

3. date   dot

_____

- - - - - - - - - - - - - - - - - -

_____

4. they   their

_____

- - - - - - - - - - - - - - - - - -

_____

5. man   mane

_____

- - - - - - - - - - - - - - - - - -

_____

6. lake   lack

_____

- - - - - - - - - - - - - - - - - -

_____

Directions: Have students circle the words said and then copy the word.

7. **ra**te   **ra**ke

8. b<u>e</u>   b**ee**s

9. s**ale**   st**ale**

10. h<u>e</u>   h**ee**l

11. tr**a**de   track

12. pl**ate**   p**ale**

Skates

Directions: Have students reread the story and answer the questions.

1. __When__ did **J**a**de** get sk**a**te**s**?

_____

- -

_____

_____

_____

_____

2. __What__ is one thing Scott asks **J**a**de**?

_____

- -

_____

_____

_____

_____

3. Which kid slips once?

_____

- -

_____

_____

- -

_____

_____

_____

- -

_____

Dear Family Member,

This is a story your child has read at school. Encourage your child to read the story to you, and then talk about it together. The bolded letters 'a-e' are a new spelling your child is learning.

Cake and Grapes

Scott got a **cake** to sh**are** with his pal J**ade**. J**ade** got a bunch of red gr**ape**s to sh**are** with Scott.

Scott went to J**ade**'s and g**ave** J**ade** the c**ake**. J**ade** g**ave** Scott the gr**ape**s. Then the kids sat and **ate**. J**ade** **ate** <u>a</u>ll of Scott's c**ake**. Scott **ate** <u>a</u>ll of J**ade**'s gr**ape**s.

Directions: Have students trace and copy the words. Students should say the sounds while writing the spellings.

i_e as in time

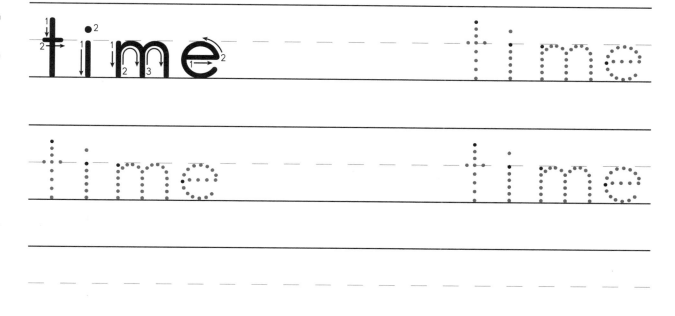

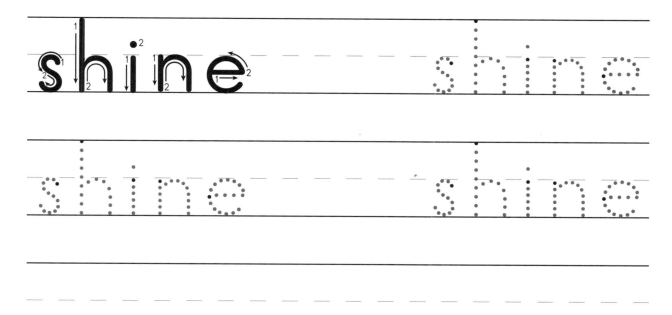

In the box <u>are</u> the names of the 4 things. Print the names on the lines.

bike	**slide**
bride	**smile**

_____

- - - - - - - - - - - - - - -

_____

_____

- - - - - - - - - - - - - - -

_____

_____

- - - - - - - - - - - - - - -

_____

_____

- - - - - - - - - - - - - - -

_____

hike

Directions: Have students copy the word on the line. Students should illustrate at least one meaning of the word.

mile

Directions: Have students copy the word on the line. Students should illustrate at least one meaning of the word.

Name _____

Dear Family Member,

This is a story your child has read at school. Encourage your child to read the story to you, and then talk about it together.

Fun in the Sand

Scott is with Jade and Dave. The kids dig in the sand. They shape the sand. They make a sand man.

A big wave hits. The kids can't save their sand man from the wave. The sand man gets wet. He slumps. He sags. He drips.

The sand man is a mess. But the kids are not sad. They run and splash in the waves.

bike	likes	cake

_____

1. She _____ hide and

seek and the slide.

2. Dan r**o**de his _____

to Sam's.

3. Yum! That is a sw**ee**t

_____

_____ !

Directions: Have students write each word on the line where it fits best.

Unit 10   55
© 2013 Core Knowledge Foundation

time	tree	trades

4. He likes grapes, and she

_____

- - - - - - -

_____ .

5. A swing hangs from

_____

- - - - - - -

the _____ .

6. Can she tell me what

_____

- - - - - - -

_____ it is?

A Fine Hike

1. <u>Where</u> did Cl**ive**'s dad set up the tent?

_____
- -
_____
_____
- -
_____
_____
- -
_____

2. <u>Wh</u>en did Scott and Cl**ive** h**ike** to the l**a**k**e** to fish?

◯ at f**ive**

◯ at n**ine**

◯ at six

Directions: Have students reread the story and answer the questions.

3. <u>What</u> did Clive's dad make?

Directions: In the box, have students illustrate a part of the story and then write a caption below.

pride

Directions: Have students copy the word on the line. Students should illustrate at least one meaning of the word.

© 2013 Core Knowledge Foundation

Name _____

Dear Family Member,

Have your child read and copy each word under the matching picture. If necessary, identify the pictures for your child.

1. b**ik**e

2. n**in**e

9   8

3. d**im**e

4. kit**e**

5. fir**e**

6. slid**e**

rid   **r**i**de**

kit   **k**i**te**

win   **w**i**ne**

slid   **sl**i**de**

rip   **r**i**pe**

twin   **tw**i**ne**

Directions: Ask students to circle the word matching the picture.

fin   **fine**

sit   **site**

dim   **dime**

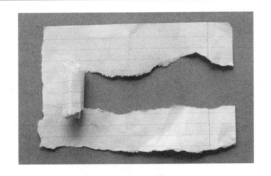

rip   **ripe**

spin   **spine**

shin   **shine**

The Bike Ride

1. Meg's t**ir**e hit . . .

⚪ a branch.

⚪ a bump.

⚪ a rock.

2. Which kid fell? Tell what that kid did when they fell.

_____

- - - - - - - - - - - - - - - - -

_____
_____

- - - - - - - - - - - - - - - - -

_____
_____

- - - - - - - - - - - - - - - - -

_____
_____

- - - - - - - - - - - - - - - - -

_____

Directions: Have students reread the story and answer the questions.

3. <u>Wh</u>at m**a**de Meg sm**ile** with pr**ide**?

Directions: In the box, have students illustrate a part of the story and then write a caption below.

Name _____

Dear Family Member,

This is a story your child has read at school. Encourage your child to read the story to you, and then talk about it together.

Skates

Jade got skates when she was six. Scott just got his last week. He is scared to get up on his skates.

"Is this safe?" Scott asks. "What if I trip and get a scrape? What if I hit a tree? What if I see a snake?"

"It is safe!" says Jade. "Just skate."

Jade helps Scott skate. Scott slips once. Then he gets the hang of it.

"Jade," he yells, "it's fun to skate!"

The Plane Ride

1. <u>Wh</u>at did Scott and Meg r<u>ide</u> in?

_____

- - - - - - - - - - - - - - - - - -

_____

_____

- - - - - - - - - - - - - - - - - -

_____

2. <u>Wh</u>ich kid s<u>ai</u>d that Big L**a**k**e** did not s**ee**m s<u>o</u> big?

_____

- - - - - - - - - - - - - - - - - -

_____

_____

- - - - - - - - - - - - - - - - - -

_____

Directions: Have students reread the story and answer the questions.

3. Meg s<u>ai</u>d the truck w<u>a</u>s the s**iz**e of a . . .

◯ pl**a**n**e**.

◯ van.

◯ dot.

rent

Directions: Have students copy the word on the line. Students should illustrate at least one meaning of the word.

strip

Dear Family Member,

Your child has been taught to read words with the separated digraphs 'a_e' as in *cake*, 'i_e' as in *time*, and the double-letter spelling 'ee' as in *keep*. Words with separated digraphs are hard to read at first because the reader has to recognize that even though the spelling for the vowel sound is separated by a consonant, the separated letters represent a single sound. Ask your child to cut out the word cards. Show the cards to your child and have your child read them. Extension: You read a word aloud and have your child write down the sounds, one at a time, paying attention to the separated digraphs. Please keep and use the cards for future practice.

tribe	speech	drive
shape	sweet	chime
free	crate	bake
flame	prize	flee

1. Can a **rake** run?

_____

2. Is it **time** to get
in bed?

_____

3. Is a sm**ile** the s**ame**
as a grin?

_____

4. Is a squ**are** a sh**ape**?

_____

5. Can a gr**ape** sing?

_____

6. Is theft a cr**ime**?

_____

7. Is a lime green?

8. Is cake sweet?

9. Can a vase jump?

10. Can a snake ride a bike?

11. Can a dog skate?

12. Can an ox ride a hen?

Directions: Have students copy and then write from memory each Tricky Word.

1.

2.

3.

4.

5.

6.

7.

they	my	by

Directions: Have students write each word on the line where it fits best.

1. I like _____ name a lot.

2. The bike is _____ the

shed.

3. The kids are sad

_____ can't skate.

their	he	me

4. If I chase the cat, it will

be scared of _____ .

_____

5. The men got _____

hats at that shop.

_____

6. James is glad that _____

can swim.

Dear Family Member,

This is a story your child has read at school. Encourage your child to read the story to you, and then talk about it together. The bolded letters 'i-e' are a new spelling your child is learning.

A Fine Hike

Scott is on a **hike** with Cl**ive** and Cl**ive**'s dad. Th**ey hike** thr**ee** m**ile**s up a big hill.

At the top of the hill, Cl**ive**'s dad says, "This is <u>where</u> w<u>e</u> will camp." H<u>e</u> drops his pack on the grass. Scott and Cl**ive** help him set up the tent.

At five, Scott and Clive hike to the lake to fish. They get five fish!

At dusk, the kids hike back to camp. Clive's dad makes a fire. The kids munch on hot dogs.

At nine, they get in their tent. They are all tired. They smile as they sleep.

o_e as in home

home   home

home   home

stone   stone

stone   stone

Print the w<u>or</u>d <u>where</u> it fits best.

1. h**o**me

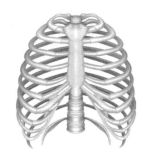

_____

- - - - - - - - - - - - - - - -

_____

_____

- - - - - - - - - - - - - - - -

_____

2. n**o**se

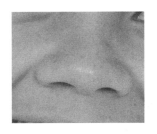

_____

- - - - - - - - - - - - - - - -

_____

_____

- - - - - - - - - - - - - - - -

_____

3. r**o**se

_____

- - - - - - - - - - - - - - - -

_____

_____

- - - - - - - - - - - - - - - -

_____

cash

Directions: Have students copy the word on the line. Students should illustrate at least one meaning of the word.

Name _____

Dear Family Member,

This is a story your child has read at school. Encourage your child to read the story to you, and then talk about it together.

The Bike Ride

Scott's sis, Meg, likes to ride a bike. Once Meg went on a bike ride with Scott. Meg's tire hit a rock and she fell off the bike.

Meg was brave. She did not yell. She did not sob. She got back on the bike. Then she said, "Let's ride!"

"Meg," Scott said, "I am glad my sis is so brave!"

That made Meg smile with pride!

| hope | made | time |

_____

1. It is _____ to get in

bed.

_____

2. We _____ a sw**ee**t

c**a**k**e**.

_____

3. I _____ Dad will let

m**e** get a dog!

Directions: Have students write each word on the line where it fits best.

bone	see	broke

4. The glass fell and
_____

- - - - - - - - - -

_____ .

5. Stan gave the dog a
_____

- - - - - - - - - -

_____ .

                                    _____

6. When will we _____

him next?

The Gift

1. <u>Wh</u>at is the **name** of the shop that Liz went to?

◯ H**o**p**e**'s Doll Shop

◯ H**o**p**e**'s Hat Shop

◯ H**o**p**e**'s Dress Shop

2. <u>Wh</u>at did Liz get Meg?

_____

- - - - - - - - - - - - - - - - - - - -

_____

- - - - - - - - - - - - - - - - - - - -

_____

- - - - - - - - - - - - - - - - - - - -

_____

3. <u>Why</u> w<u>a</u>s H**o**p**e** glad?

_____

- -

_____

_____

- -

_____

_____

- -

_____

The Sled Ride

1. Which kid got on the sled last? Where did that kid sit?

2. What did the sled hit?

3. <u>W</u>hich b**o**n**e**s did J**a**d**e** f**ee**l like sh<u>e</u> br**oke**?

◯ leg b**o**n**e**s

◯ hand b**o**n**e**s

◯ back b**o**n**e**s

steer

Directions: Have students copy the word on the line. Students should illustrate at least one meaning of the word.

drag

Directions: Have students copy the word on the line. Students should illustrate at least one meaning of the word.

Dear Family Member,

This is a story your child has read at school. Encourage your child to read the story to you, and then talk about it together.

The Plane Ride

Scott's dad rents a plane. He asks Scott and Meg to ride with him in the plane. The kids smile and nod.

The kids get in the plane. They click on their belts. Then their dad takes off. The plane picks up speed. By the time it gets to the end of the strip, it lifts up.

The kids can **see** lots of things fr**o**m the pl**ane**.

"That's Big L**a**ke!" says Scott. "But it's not s**o** big fr**o**m up h**ere**, is it? It s**ee**ms l**ike** it's just a frog pond!"

"What's that?" Meg asks.

"That's a truck," says Scott.

"A truck?" says Meg. "But it's the s**ize** of a dot!"

Scott and Meg sm**ile**. It's fun to r**ide** in a pl**ane**.

Name _____

hop **h**o**pe**

rob **r**o**be**

mop **m**o**pe**

cod **c**o**de**

tot **t**o**te**

rat **r**a**te**

Directions: Ask students to circle the word matching the picture.

not **note**

tap **tape**

can **cane**

con **cone**

glob **globe**

dot **dote**

1. **b**a**ke**   **b**i**ke**

2. ch**ee**k   chick

3. n**o**se   n**o**te

4. f**i**ne   fin

5. h**o**le   p**o**le

6. b**ee**   b**ee**t

7. dime   dome

_____
- - - - - - - - - - - - -
_____

8. gate   game

_____
- - - - - - - - - - - - -
_____

9. grove   grave

_____
- - - - - - - - - - - - -
_____

10. keep   kept

_____
- - - - - - - - - - - - -
_____

11. male   mile

_____
- - - - - - - - - - - - -
_____

12. rate   rat

_____
- - - - - - - - - - - - -
_____

tote bag

_____

- -

_____

Directions: Have students copy the word on the line. Students should illustrate at least one meaning of the word.

Dear Family Member,

   Your child has been taught to read several new Tricky Words and has been practicing reading words with the separated digraphs 'a_e' as in *same*, 'i_e' as in *life*, and 'o_e' as in *vote*. Ask your child to cut out the word cards and arrange them to make phrases. The phrases can make sense or be silly. Have your child read the phrases.

on	they	three
ride	are	bikes
cakes	here	we
those	my	bake

Scott's Snack Stand

1. <u>Wha</u>t did Scott get fr<u>o</u>m the shop?

⭕ a b**ike**

⭕ nuts

⭕ plums

2. <u>Wha</u>t did the nuts cost Scott?

_____

- - - - - - - - - - - - - - - - - - -

_____

_____

- - - - - - - - - - - - - - - - - - -

_____

_____

- - - - - - - - - - - - - - - - - - -

_____

3. Tell <u>what</u> Scott did with the nuts.

Directions: In the box, have students illustrate a part of the story and then write a caption below.

Dear Family Member,

This is a story your child has read at school. Encourage your child to read the story to you, and then talk about it together.

The Gift

Scott and Meg's mom is named Liz. She stops off at Hope's Dress Shop.

"Hope," Liz says, "I need a doll's dress. The dress on Meg's doll has a bunch of holes in it."

"Well," says Hope, "here's a dress. It's a doll's size, and it's on sale."

"This is just <u>what</u> I n**ee**d!" says Liz. "It will fit Meg's doll, and Meg l**i**k**e**s gr**ee**n!"

H**o**p**e** drops the dress in a bag. Liz hands H**o**p**e** cash. H**o**p**e** hands the bag to Liz.

H**o**p**e** is glad. Sh<u>e</u> has m**a**d**e** a s**a**l**e**. Liz is glad, as well. Sh<u>e</u> has a gift to t**a**k**e** h**o**m**e** to Meg.

u_e as in cute

Directions: Have students trace and copy the words. Students should say the sounds while writing the spellings.

cute   cute

cute   cute

use   use   use

use   use   use

Print the w<u>or</u>d <u>where</u> it fits best.

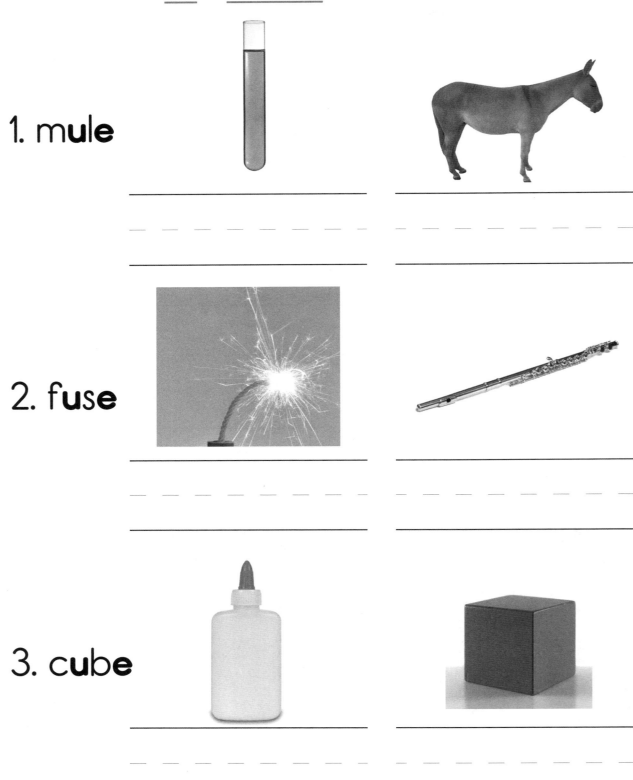

1. m**ule**

_____

·····················

_____

2. f**use**

_____

·····················

_____

3. c**ube**

_____

·····················

_____

chimp

Directions: Have students copy the word on the line. Students should illustrate at least one meaning of the word.

zone

_____

- -

_____

Directions: Have students copy the word on the line. Students should illustrate at least one meaning of the word.

Dear Family Member,

This is a story your child has read at school. Encourage your child to read the story to you, and then talk about it together.

The Sled Ride

"I'll dri**ve**!" s<u>ai</u>d Scott, as h<u>e</u> sat on the sled. J**a**d**e** and Meg got on next. D**a**v**e** w<u>a</u>s the last one on the sled. H<u>e</u> sat in back.

The sled slid off. It went fast.

"Scott," J**a**d**e** s<u>ai</u>d, "st**ee**r to the left! Th<u>ere</u>'s a big st**o**n**e** th<u>ere</u> b<u>y</u> the—"

Smack! The sled hit the st**o**n**e**. The kids fell off.

Scott went to check on J**a**de.

"Ug!" J**a**de said. "I f**ee**l l**i**ke I br**o**ke <u>a</u>ll the b**o**ne̅s i̅n m<u>y</u> leg!"

"Hop on the sled," Scott s<u>ai</u>d. "I will drag it h**o**me̅."

Meg went to check on D**a**ve.

D**a**ve s<u>ai</u>d, "I fr**o**ze̅ m<u>y</u> n**o**se!"

"Hop on the sled with J**a**de," said Meg. "Scott and I will drag it h**o**me̅."

In the Pet Shop

1. <u>What</u> is in the pen with the chimp?

_____

- -

_____

_____

- -

_____

2. <u>Why</u> can't Scott **take** the chimp h**o**m**e**?

_____

- -

_____

_____

- -

_____

3. <u>What</u> pet can Scott **take** h**o**m**e**?

◯ a chimp

◯ a dog

◯ a fish

Directions: In the box, have students illustrate a part of the story and then write a caption below.

Dear Family Member,

Have your child read and copy each word under the matching picture. If necessary, identify the pictures for your child.

cube	mule
fuse	sheep

_____

- - - - - - - - - - - - - -

_____

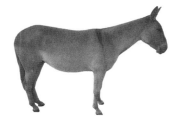

_____

- - - - - - - - - - - - - -

_____

_____

- - - - - - - - - - - - - -

_____

_____

- - - - - - - - - - - - - -

_____

| rose | fire |
| grapes | tree |

_____

- - - - - - - - - - -

_____

_____

- - - - - - - - - - -

_____

_____

- - - - - - - - - - -

_____

_____

- - - - - - - - - - -

_____

Scott Bakes a Cake

1. <u>Wha</u>t did Scott help m**ake**?

_____
- - - - - - - - - - - - - - - - - -
_____
_____
- - - - - - - - - - - - - - - - - -
_____
_____
- - - - - - - - - - - - - - - - - -
_____

2. <u>Wha</u>t did Scott crack and mix?

_____
- - - - - - - - - - - - - - - - - -
_____
_____
- - - - - - - - - - - - - - - - - -
_____
_____
- - - - - - - - - - - - - - - - - -
_____

3. <u>Wh</u>at did Scott's mom say <u>wh</u>en Scott said that he'd **like** to add the **cake** mix?

_____

- -

_____

_____

- -

_____

_____

_____

- -

_____

frost

Directions: Have students copy the word on the line. Students should illustrate at least one meaning of the word.

Dear Family Member,

This is a story your child has read at school. Encourage your child to read the story to you, and then talk about it together.

Scott's Snack Stand

Scott has a snack stand. Last week, he rode his bike to a shop to get nuts to sell at his stand. He got three big bags of nuts. The nuts cost him a lot of cash.

Scott slid the bags in his tote bag. Then he rode home.

When he got home, he got his mom to help him make hot spice nuts on the stove top.

Then Scott set up his stand.

"Hot sp**ice** nuts!" h<u>e</u> said. "Get a bag of hot sp**ice** nuts! Just one buck!"

A kid c**ame** b<u>y</u> and got a bag of nuts. Then a man got a bag. Then the man's w**ife** got a bag. H<u>e</u> m**ade** back the f**ive** h<u>e</u> had spent on nuts, plus ten in cash!

1. Are you at h**o**m**e**?

2. Can a cat **u**s**e** a pen?

3. Is a frog as big as a m**ule**?

4. Is a r**o**se a plant?

5. Is a st**o**n**e** as soft as a bed?

6. Is y**our** h**o**m**e** in a tr**ee**?

7. Can a dog dig a hole?

_____

8. Is a cube a shape?

_____

9. Is there a chimp with a green nose in this class?

_____

10. Is a rope a lot like a string?

_____

11. Can you smile?

_____

12. Is there a kid in this class with no bones?

_____

1.

2.

3.

4.

5.

6.

7.

Directions: Have students copy and then write from memory each Tricky Word.

so	no	your

Directions: Have students write each word on the line where it fits best.

1. Mom said yes, but Dad

said _____ .

2. Is this _____ cake?

3. That r**o**se is _____ big!

you	my	by

4. Did the dog like _____ ?

5. There is a stone _____ the path.

6. This is _____ home.

1.   chop   ship   shop   shot

2.   smack   mash   mesh   smash

3.   quit   bench   queen   quench

4.   then   sing   thin   thing

5.   them   thug   thump   trip

6. tee   trade   tree   free

7. poke   Jade   junk   joke

8. wake   wade   wide   woke

9. fine   fire   five   fish

10. cut   cute   kite   cube

1. what   where   was   were

2. here   were   where   when

3. why   which   when   what

4. all   a   are   the

5. they   your   the   their

6. you   why   no   your

7. me   she   he   be

8. one   once   from   word

9. so   from   of   one

10. their   says   said   so

Kindergarten CKLA End-of-Year Summary

Record the following information, and place Worksheets 26.1, 26.2, and 27.1 in a folder for next year's teacher.

Student Name:	
Date:	
Kindergarten Teacher Name:	

Recommended Placement for Next Year (check one)

_____	**On Level**	_____	**Slightly Below Level**
_____	**Above Level**	_____	**Needs Intensive Remediation**

Assessment Scores

_____ %	**Worksheet 26.1: Part 1A Decodable Word Reading Score (___ /10)**
	Worksheet 26.2: Part 1B Tricky Word Score (___ /10)
_____ %	**Worksheet 27.1: Part 2 Sound Writing Score (___ /15)**
_____ %	**Worksheet 27.5: If needed, Part 3 Individually Administered Letter Sounds Score (___ /35)**
Optional _____ %	**Worksheet 28.1: Part 4 Writing Lowercase Letters (___ /26)** (This is an optional assessment and is not included in the End-of-Year Student Performance Task Assessment Scoring Interpretation.)
Optional _____ %	**Worksheet 28.2: Part 5 Uppercase Letter Names (___ /26)** (This is an optional assessment and is not included in the End-of-Year Student Performance Task Assessment Scoring Interpretation.)

Missed Tricky Words from Worksheet 26.1 (list words)

_____   _____   _____   _____   _____

_____   _____   _____   _____   _____

_____   _____   _____   _____   _____

Missed Spellings from Worksheet 26.2 (list spellings)

_____   _____   _____   _____   _____

_____   _____   _____   _____   _____

_____   _____   _____   _____   _____

If Needed, Missed Sounds from Worksheet 27.1 (list sounds)

_____   _____   _____   _____   _____

_____   _____   _____   _____   _____

_____   _____   _____   _____   _____

_____   _____   _____   _____   _____

_____   _____   _____   _____   _____

_____   _____   _____   _____   _____

The Cave

1. **Where** **are** Scott and J**a**d**e**?

   ◯ at a l**a**k**e**

   ◯ on a pl**a**n**e**

   ◯ in a c**a**v**e**

2. **Wh**ich kid l**i**k**e**s bats?

   _____
   - - - - - - - - - - - - - - - - -
   _____
   _____
   - - - - - - - - - - - - - - - - -
   _____
   _____
   - - - - - - - - - - - - - - - - -
   _____

Directions: Have students reread the story and answer the questions.

3. Tell what Jade yells.

Directions: In the box, have students illustrate a part of the story and then write a caption below.

peek

_____

- -

_____

glide

Directions: Have students copy the word on the line. Students should illustrate at least one meaning of the word.

dip

Directions: Have students copy the word on the line. Students should illustrate at least one meaning of the word.

In the Pet Shop

Scott is in a pet shop. He spots a chimp in a pen. The chimp hangs from a branch. Then he jumps up on a big red **cube** and grins at Scott.

Scott sings a **tune** to the chimp. The chimp w**a**ve**s** back. Scott **like**s the chimp, and the chimp s**ee**ms to **like** him!

"Mom," Scott says, "this chimp is s<u>o</u> c**ute**. He got up on his c**ube** and w**a**v**e**d at m<u>e</u>! Can I t**ake** him h**o**m**e**?"

"No," says his mom. "M<u>y</u> h**ome** is a chimp-fr**ee** z**one**."

Scott st**are**s at the chimp. His mom can s**ee** that he is sad, s<u>o</u> sh<u>e</u> tells him he can get a fish.

Scott is so sad he can't t**ake** the chimp h**ome**, but he is glad he gets to t**ake** a fish h**ome**.

1. _____

2. _____

3. _____

4. _____

5. _____

6. _____

7. _____

8. _____

9. _____

10. _____

11. _____

12. _____

13. _____

14. _____

15. _____

The Skiff Ride

1. <u>Wh</u>at is a skiff?

_____

- - - - - - - - - - - - - - - - - - - -

_____

_____

_____

- - - - - - - - - - - - - - - - - - - -

_____

2. <u>Wh</u>ich kid st**ee**rs the skiff?

_____

- - - - - - - - - - - - - - - - - - - -

_____

_____

- - - - - - - - - - - - - - - - - - - -

_____

_____

Directions: Have students reread the story and answer the questions.

3. List the things that Ling spots.

- -

_____

_____

_____

_____

- -

_____

Directions: In the box, have students illustrate a part of the story and then write a caption below.

_____

- -

_____

skiff

Directions: Have students copy the word on the line. Students should illustrate at least one meaning of the word.

crane

Directions: Have students copy the word on the line. Students should illustrate at least one meaning of the word.

Unit 10   161
© 2013 Core Knowledge Foundation

Dear Family Member,

This is a story your child has read at school. Encourage your child to read the story to you, and then talk about it together.

Scott Bakes a Cake

Scott's mom b**a**ke**s** c**a**ke**s** with Meg.

"Scott," she says, "you can help us with this c**a**k**e**, if you like."

Scott shrugs. "Well," he says, "if you can **use** my help, I will help."

"It will be fun," says his mom. "You can crack the eggs."

Scott cracks thr**ee** eggs and drops them in the dish.

Scott asks if he can mix up the eggs. Then he asks if he can add in the c**a**k**e** mix.

"Well," his mom says, "if y<u>ou</u> add the c**a**k**e** mix, then Meg gets to frost the c**a**k**e**."

"Can I help Meg frost it?" Scott asks.

Mom and Meg sm**i**l**e**.

Meg says, "S**ee**, Scott. It's fun to b**a**k**e** a c**a**k**e**!"

1. _____ 'm' > /m/ as in *mat*

2. _____ 'a' > /a/ as in *at*

3. _____ 't' > /t/ as in *tip*

4. _____ 'd' > /d/ as in *dig*

5. _____ 'o' > /o/ as in *odd*

6. _____ 'c' > /k/ as in *cat*

7. _____ 'g' > /g/ as in *get*

8. _____ 'i' > /i/ as in *it*

9. _____ 'n' > /n/ as in *nut*

10. _____ 'h' > /h/ as in *hug*

11. _____ 's' > /s/ as in *sit*

12. _____ 'f' > /f/ as in *fun*

13. _____ 'v' > /v/ as in *van*

14. _____ 'z' > /z/ as in *zip*

15. _____ 'p' > /p/ as in *pet*

16. _____ 'e' > /e/ as in *end*

17. _____ 'b' > /b/ as in *bug*

18. _____ 'l' > /l/ as in *leg*

19. _____ 'r' > /r/ as in *red*

20. _____ 'u' > /u/ as in *up*

21. _____ 'w' > /w/ as in *wet*

22. _____ 'j' > /j/ as in *job*

23. _____ 'y' > /y/ as in *yes*

24. _____ 'x' > /x/ as in *box*

25. _____ 'k' > /k/ as in *kid*

16. _____ 'ch' > /ch/ as in *chip*

27. _____ 'sh' > /sh/ as in *ship*

28. _____ 'th' > /th/ as in *thin* or /th/ as in *this*

29. _____ 'qu' > /qu/ as in *quit*

30. _____ 'ng' > /ng/ as in *sing*

31. _____ 'ss' > /s/ as in *toss*

32. _____ 'ck' > /k/ as in *rock*

33. _____ 'll' > /l/ as in *bill*

34. _____ 'ff' > /f/ as in *stuff*

35. _____ 'ee' > /ee/ as in *bee*

Total correct _____/35

1. _____

2. _____

3. _____

4. _____

5. _____

6. _____

7. _____

8. _____

9. _____

10. _____

11. _____

12. _____

13. _____

14. _____

15. _____

16. _____

17. _____

18. _____

19. _____

20. _____

21. _____

22. _____

23. _____

24. _____

25. _____

26. _____

1.	A	W	E	I
2.	T	Y	U	W
3.	O	P	T	M
4.	F	G	H	N
5.	K	L	Z	C
6.	C	B	S	D
7.	D	X	Z	B
8.	N	I	H	M
9.	C	R	N	M
10.	L	Y	P	G
11.	E	A	I	W
12.	N	H	T	K
13.	B	D	P	Q

14.	R	L	T	F
15.	S	T	M	K
16.	X	V	T	Z
17.	I	T	J	L
18.	Y	I	J	F
19.	I	E	U	J
20.	B	O	D	Q
21.	Z	S	N	T
22.	N	M	Q	K
23.	Z	U	W	D
24.	T	A	G	E
25.	U	B	V	D
26.	A	W	E	X

1.    n**ose**   h**ose**   r**ose**

2. 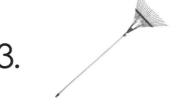   sh**ee**p   f**ee**t   b**ee**t

3.    c**a**ve   l**a**ke   r**a**ke

4.    b**i**te   b**ee**t   b**i**ke

5.    l**i**me   k**i**te   d**i**me

Directions: For each picture, have students circle the matching word.

6. rope   hope   ripe

7. teeth   teen   tree

8. rate   rake   lake

9. home   rope   robe

10. mute   mule   fume

Dear Family Member,

This is a story your child has read at school. Encourage your child to read the story to you, and then talk about it together.

The Cave

Scott and Jade are on a hike. Jade spots a cave and peeks in.

"Are there bats in there?" Scott asks.

"I can't tell," Jade says, "but I hope so! I like bats!"

"Ick!" says Scott. "Bats are not cute."

Scott and Jade step in the cave.

Jade yells, "Bats, <u>where</u> <u>are</u> <u>you</u>? Wake up!"

Scott says, "Let the bats sleep."

Just then a bat glides up. It flaps its wings. It dips and spins.

Jade stares at the bat and smiles.

Scott ducks and yells, "Hide! A bat!"

Lunch Trades

1. What is in Dave's lunch bag?

_____

- - - - - - - - - - - - - - - - -

_____
_____

- - - - - - - - - - - - - - - - -

_____
_____

- - - - - - - - - - - - - - - - -

_____

2. What will Ling trade?

◯ a hot dog

◯ chips

◯ ham

3. <u>What</u> things <u>are</u> in Scott's lunch bag?

◯ a fish bone, lump of fat, and a wet sock

◯ chips, ham, a bun, and red gr**a**p**e**s

◯ chips, a can of pop, and gr**a**p**e**s

Directions: In the box, have students illustrate a part of the story and then write a caption below.

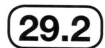

Dear Family Member,

This is a story your child has read at school. Encourage your child to read the story to you, and then talk about it together.

The Skiff Ride

"Let's **take** a **ri**d**e** in m**y** skiff," says Scott.

"What's a skiff?" asks Ling.

"Um, it's **like** a ship," says Scott, "but not s**o** big."

The kids run to the dock. Th**ey** can swim well, but, to b**e** s**afe**, they slip on **life** vests. Scott and Ling get in the skiff.

Scott steers the skiff. He steers it to the west side of the lake. The skiff glides in the wind.

Ling spots lots of fun things.

"I see ducks by that pine tree!" she yells.

"Is that a fish?" Scott asks.

"There's a crane!" Ling adds.

She says, "Scott, this is so much fun!"

Directions: For each word, have students count the sounds. Have students write the number of sounds in the box and copy the word on the line.

1. sm**ile**

2. tr**ee**

3. br**a**ke

4. h**o**le

5. sh**a**de

6. sp**i**ke

7. ch**o**ke

8. rope ☐ _____

9. bride ☐ _____

10. cone ☐ _____

11. sleep ☐ _____

12. plane ☐ _____

13. bee ☐ _____

14. size ☐ _____

Check the words that are the best fit.

1.
   ○ Jane has a kite.
   ○ Jane has a bike.

2.
   ○ My cat is cute.
   ○ My hat is cute.

3.
   ○ This is a rose.
   ○ This is a nose.

4.
   ○ His sheep smell.
   ○ His feet smell.

5.
   ○ She is at the lake.
   ○ She is in bed.

6.

○ Dave **r**a**ke**s the grass.

○ Dave **b**a**ke**s ham.

7.

○ He s**ee**ms sad.

○ He s**ee**ms glad.

8.

○ Th**ose** <u>are</u> fish.

○ Th**ose** <u>are</u> pigs.

9.

○ He has a c**ute** pup.

○ He has a c**ute** cat.

10.

○ Th**ey** sit and sm**ile**.

○ Th**ey** sit on b**ike**s.

Make a line from the words to the things.

1. sheep

2. bike

3. tape

4. cube

5. snake

6. trees

7. d**ee**r

8. sl**i**d**e**

9. pl**a**t**e**

10. c**a**n**e**

11. c**o**n**e**

12. b**ee**

Directions: Have students circle the phrases that are read aloud.

1. a red fl**a**m**e**   a red fr**a**m**e**

2. h<u>e</u> runs in   sh<u>e</u> runs in

3. pass the c**o**n**e**   pass the c**a**n**e**

4. th<u>eir</u> b**i**k**e**s   the b**i**k**e**s

5. a h**i**v**e** of b**ee**s   b**ee**s in a h**i**v**e**

6. <u>you</u> and Mom   <u>your</u> mom

7. w**a**k**e** him up   w**o**k**e** him up

8. th<u>ey</u> <u>are</u> m**ute**   th<u>ey</u> <u>are</u> **c**ute

9. a lot of f**ee**t   a lot of f**ee**d

10. the gr**ee**n tin   the gr**ee**n lime

11. sh**ade** of red   **d**ash of red

12. on this s**ide**   on this s**ite**

mop

m**o**p**e**

cap

c**a**p**e**

fin

f**i**n**e**

Directions: Have students circle the words matching the pictures.

kit

k**i**t**e**

cut

c**u**t**e**

not

n**o**t**e**

man

mane

cub

cube

rob

robe

ten

teen

pin

pine

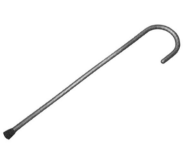

can

cane

Dear Family Member,

This is a story your child has read at school. Encourage your child to read the story to you, and then talk about it together.

Lunch Trades

Dave checks his lunch bag. "No!" he fumes. "It's ham. I **ate** ham all week! Will y<u>ou</u> tr**a**de, Ling?"

"I'll tr**a**de m<u>y</u> hot dog," Ling says, "but not m<u>y</u> chips. Will y<u>ou</u> tr**a**de y<u>our</u> lunch, Scott?"

"I will tr**a**de," Scott says, "but y<u>ou</u> will not **like** <u>what</u> Mom g**a**ve m<u>e</u>."

"Why?" asks Ling. "What's in your bag?"

"A fish bone, a lump of fat, and a wet sock," says Scott.

"No to all of those!" says Ling.

"Ug!" says Dave. "No trade!"

As Ling and Dave trade, Scott keeps his bag. He does not tell Ling and Dave what he has in his bag. He has chips, ham, a bun, and a bunch of red grapes. Scott likes all of the things in his bag. He will not trade them.

Dear Family Member,

This is a story your child has read at school. Encourage your child to read the story to you, and then talk about it together.

Mike's Tale

The kids sat by a fire.

"Let's all tell tales," said Ling. "Then we can vote on which tale is the best!"

"Let me tell mine!" Mike said. "My tale will scare you."

"No!" said Dave, "You can't scare me!"

"Well," said Mike, "we will see!" "There's a grump," Mike said, "that makes its home close to this spot. It's big. It has long fangs. It sleeps when the sun is up and wakes when the sun sets. The grump can smell kids. It likes to grab them and . . ."

Just then, there was a snap.

"What was that?" Dave said.

"It was just a twig," Ling said.

"But what made it snap like that?" said Dave.

Dave was scared.

"EEEEEEEEEEEEEEEE!" he said. "IT'S THE GRUMP! RUN! RUN FROM THE GRUMP!"

Dave got up to run, but Ling said, "It's not the Grump! It's just Meg!"

Dear Family Member,

This is a story your child has read at school. Encourage your child to read the story to you, and then talk about it together.

Green Grove Glade

Dave and Scott hike to Green Grove Glade with their moms and dads.

They stop at the gate and a man says, "Moms and dads, rest here where you can see your kids as they run, jump, and slide."

Scott and Dave are glad this is a spot for kids. They are glad their moms and dads are close if they get tired.

The kids swing on the swings. They slide on the slides. They ride on the rides. When they get tired, they get their moms and dads and hike back to their homes.

"Was it fun, Scott?" his mom asks when they get home.

Scott nods and smiles.

"What was it like?" she asks.

Scott grins and quips, "It was fun, Mom! Green Grove Glade is a fun spot for kids!"

Dear Family Member,

This is a story your child has read at school. Encourage your child to read the story to you, and then talk about it together.

The Boss

"Meg," Scott says, "when Mom and Dad are on their trip, I will be the boss here."

"You are not the boss of me!" says Meg.

"I'm the boss!" says Scott.

"You are not!" says Meg.

Scott glares at Meg. Meg glares back at him. Just then Mom steps in and taps Scott on the back. "Scott," she says, "meet Jen. Jen will be the boss till Dad and I get back."

"Meg's boss?" Scott asks.

"Meg's boss and Scott's boss," his mom says.

"Rats!" says Scott. "When will I get to be the boss?"

Dear Family Member,

This is a story your child has read at school. Encourage your child to read the story to you, and then talk about it together.

The King of Kites

"What's that?" D**a**ve asks.

"It's a k**ite** I m**a**de," says Scott.

"Can I help y<u>ou</u> test it?" D**a**ve asks.

"Yes," says Scott.

The kids take the kite cl**o**se to the lake to test it. Scott grabs the string. Then he runs as fast as he can.

The wind grabs Scott's kite. The kite zips up. It rides on the wind. It shines in the sun. The wind lifts it up till it is just a speck.

Dave cheers.

"Scott," he yells, "you are the man! That kite you made is the best kite of all time! You are the King of Kites!"

Mike's Tale

1. <u>Wh</u>ich kid had a **tale** to tell?

_____

- - - - - - - - - - - - - - - -

_____

_____

_____

- - - - - - - - - - - - - - - -

_____

2. <u>Wha</u>t sc**a**r**e**d D**a**v**e**?

_____

- - - - - - - - - - - - - - - -

_____

_____

- - - - - - - - - - - - - - - -

_____

- - - - - - - - - - - - - - - -

_____

Directions: Have students reread the story and answer the questions.

3. <u>What made</u> the twig snap?

◯ the grump

◯ Meg

◯ Mike

Directions: In the box, have students illustrate a part of the story and write a caption below.

Green Grove Glade

1. <u>What</u> is Green Grove Glade?

_____

- - - - - - - - - - - - - - - - - -

_____

- - - - - - - - - - - - - - - - - -

_____

- - - - - - - - - - - - - - - - - -

_____

2. <u>What</u> is one fun thing at Green Grove Glade?

_____

- - - - - - - - - - - - - - - - - -

_____

- - - - - - - - - - - - - - - - - -

_____

- - - - - - - - - - - - - - - - - -

_____

3. <u>What</u> will Scott tell his mom Gr**ee**n Gr**o**ve is l**i**ke?

_____

- -

_____

_____

- -

_____

_____

- -

_____

Directions: In the box, have students illustrate a part of the story and write a caption below.

_____

- -

_____

The Boss

1. <u>Wh</u>at m**a**d**e** Meg mad?

_____

- -

_____

_____

- -

_____

2. Tell <u>wh</u>at Mom said to Scott.

_____

- -

_____

_____

- -

_____

Directions: Have students reread the story and answer the questions.

3. <u>What</u> is a boss?

_____

- - - - - - - - - - - - - - - - - -

_____
_____

- - - - - - - - - - - - - - - - - -

_____
_____

- - - - - - - - - - - - - - - - - -

_____

Directions: In the box, have students illustrate a part of the story and write a caption below.

_____

- - - - - - - - - - - - - - - - - -

_____

The King of Kites

1. What did Scott make?

_____
- -
_____
- -
_____
- -
_____

2. Where did Scott and Dave test the kite?

_____
- -
_____
- -
_____
- -
_____

Directions: Have students reread the story and answer the questions.

3. Dave said Scott is . . .

◯ the King of Kites.

◯ the Kite Kid.

◯ the Kite Man.

Directions: Have students reread the story "Scott Bakes a Cake" and have students paste the sentences onto Worksheet PP16 in the correct order.

Scott cracks thr**ee** eggs and drops them in the dish, one by one.

Mom tells Scott that he can help m**ake** the c**ake**.

Meg says, "S**ee**, Scott. It's fun to b**ake** a c**ake**!"

Scott asks Mom if he can add in the c**ake** mix.

Name _____

Directions: Have students paste the sentences from Worksheet PP15 on this worksheet in the correct order. Then have students illustrate each sentence.

1.

2.

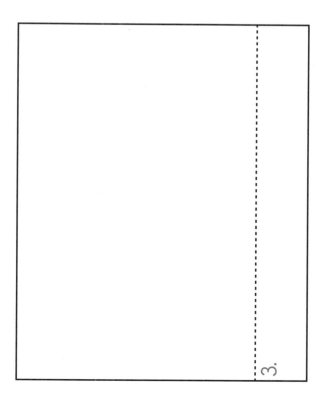

3.

4.

Fill in the gaps.

1. c___t___

2. c___t

3. b___t

4. b___t

5. b___t___

6. b___k___

7. b___k___

8. w___k___

9. w___k___

10. ch___k___

spin	spine
shin	pine
quit	pin
shine	quite

as in b<u>i</u>t

as in b<u>i</u>t<u>e</u>

Directions: Have students write the words containing the /i/ sound spelled 'i' under the 'i' header and the words containing the /ie/ sound spelled 'i_e' under the 'i_e' header.

cub	cube
us	fuzz
m**ute**	**us**e
f**use**	mutt

as in c<u>u</u>t

as in c<u>u</u>t<u>e</u>

_____

- - - - - - - - - - - - - -

_____

- - - - - - - - - - - - - -

_____

- - - - - - - - - - - - - -

_____

- - - - - - - - - - - - - -

_____

Print the w<u>o</u>rd <u>where</u> it fits best.

1. c**a**ke

_____   _____

- - - - - - - - - - - - - -   - - - - - - - - - - - - - -

_____   _____

2. b**i**k**e**

_____   _____

- - - - - - - - - - - - - -   - - - - - - - - - - - - - -

_____   _____

3. r**o**b**e**

_____   _____

- - - - - - - - - - - - - -   - - - - - - - - - - - - - -

_____   _____

4. cube

_____   _____
- - - - - - - - - - - - - -   - - - - - - - - - - - - - -
_____   _____

5. cane

_____   _____
- - - - - - - - - - - - - -   - - - - - - - - - - - - - -
_____   _____

6. smile

_____   _____
- - - - - - - - - - - - - -   - - - - - - - - - - - - - -
_____   _____

Print the n**a**m**e**s of the things.

grape gr**a**de

_____

- - - - - - - - - - - - - - - - - - -

_____

h**o**me hand

_____

- - - - - - - - - - - - - - - - - - -

_____

frill f**ire**

_____

- - - - - - - - - - - - - - - - - - -

_____

m**u**te m**u**le

_____

- - - - - - - - - - - - - - - - - - -

_____

dime deem		clap cape

_____

- - - - - - - - - - - -

_____

_____

- - - - - - - - - - - -

_____

hose nose		gate rake

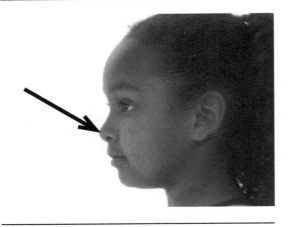

_____

- - - - - - - - - - - -

_____

_____

- - - - - - - - - - - -

_____

In the box <u>are</u> the names of the 6 things. Print the names on the lines.

lake	globe
feet	mule
bike	snake

Directions: Have students write each word under its matching picture.

_____

_____

_____

_____

_____

_____

_____

_____

_____

_____

_____

_____

cone	grapes
cube	bones
sleep	bride

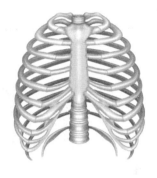

_____

- - - - - - - - - - - -

_____

_____

- - - - - - - - - - - -

_____

Name _____

rope   nose

cone   stone

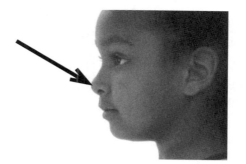

_____   _____

- - - - - - - - - - - - - - - - - - -   - - - - - - - - - - - - - - - - - - -

_____   _____

_____   _____

- - - - - - - - - - - - - - - - - - -   - - - - - - - - - - - - - - - - - - -

_____   _____

Directions: Ask students to write the matching word under the picture.

home	bones
robe	rose

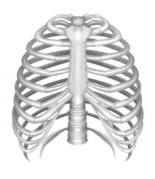

_____

- - - - - - - - - - - - -

_____

_____

- - - - - - - - - - - - -

_____

_____

- - - - - - - - - - - - -

_____

_____

- - - - - - - - - - - - -

_____

Print the words.

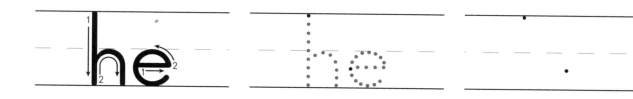

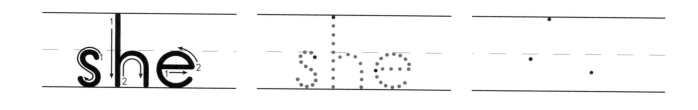

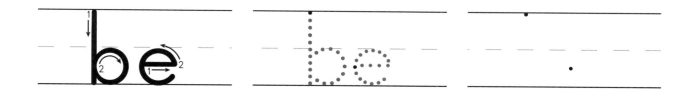

Print the words.

they

they

they

their

their

their

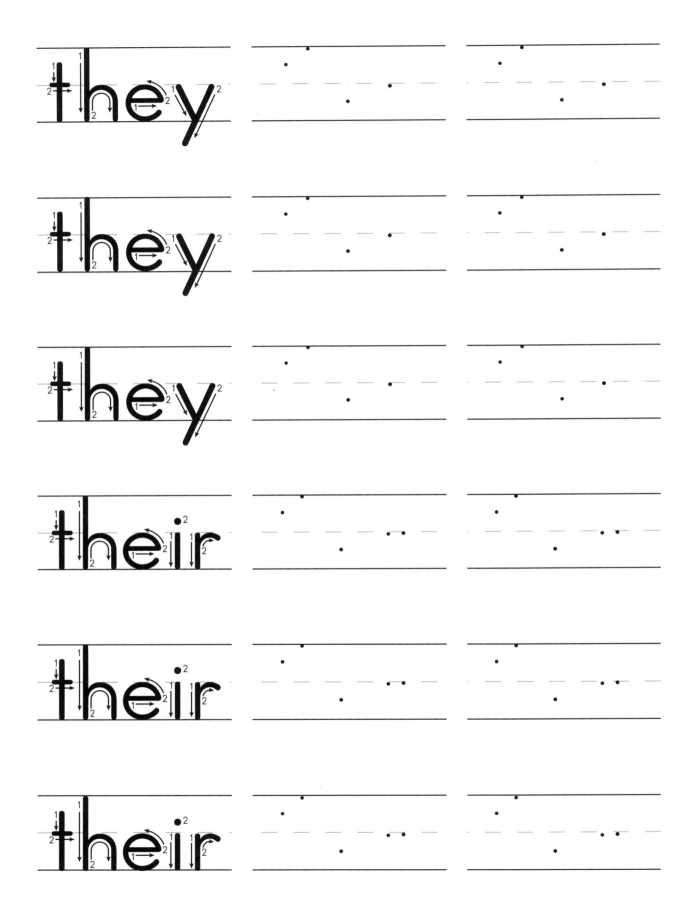

they

they

they

their

their

their

Print the words.

my   my   _____

by   by   _____

you   you   _____

you   you   _____

your your _____

your your _____

my

by

you

you

your

your

CORE KNOWLEDGE LANGUAGE ARTS

SERIES EDITOR-IN-CHIEF
E. D. Hirsch, Jr.

PRESIDENT
Linda Bevilacqua

EDITORIAL STAFF
Carolyn Gosse, Senior Editor - Preschool
Khara Turnbull, Materials Development Manager
Michelle L. Warner, Senior Editor - Listening & Learning

Mick Anderson
Robin Blackshire
Maggie Buchanan
Paula Coyner
Sue Fulton
Sara Hunt
Erin Kist
Robin Luecke
Rosie McCormick
Cynthia Peng
Liz Pettit
Ellen Sadler
Deborah Samley
Diane Auger Smith
Sarah Zelinke

DESIGN AND GRAPHICS STAFF
Scott Ritchie, Creative Director

Kim Berrall
Michael Donegan
Liza Greene
Matt Leech
Bridget Moriarty
Lauren Pack

CONSULTING PROJECT MANAGEMENT SERVICES
ScribeConcepts.com

ADDITIONAL CONSULTING SERVICES
Ang Blanchette
Dorrit Green
Carolyn Pinkerton

ACKNOWLEDGMENTS

These materials are the result of the work, advice, and encouragement of numerous individuals over many years. Some of those singled out here already know the depth of our gratitude; others may be surprised to find themselves thanked publicly for help they gave quietly and generously for the sake of the enterprise alone. To helpers named and unnamed we are deeply grateful.

CONTRIBUTORS TO EARLIER VERSIONS OF THESE MATERIALS

Susan B. Albaugh, Kazuko Ashizawa, Nancy Braier, Kathryn M. Cummings, Michelle De Groot, Diana Espinal, Mary E. Forbes, Michael L. Ford, Ted Hirsch, Danielle Knecht, James K. Lee, Diane Henry Leipzig, Martha G. Mack, Liana Mahoney, Isabel McLean, Steve Morrison, Juliane K. Munson, Elizabeth B. Rasmussen, Laura Tortorelli, Rachael L. Shaw, Sivan B. Sherman, Miriam E. Vidaver, Catherine S. Whittington, Jeannette A. Williams

We would like to extend special recognition to Program Directors Matthew Davis and Souzanne Wright who were instrumental to the early development of this program.

SCHOOLS

We are truly grateful to the teachers, students, and administrators of the following schools for their willingness to field test these materials and for their invaluable advice: Capitol View Elementary, Challenge Foundation Academy (IN), Community Academy Public Charter School, Lake Lure Classical Academy, Lepanto Elementary School, New Holland Core Knowledge Academy, Paramount School of Excellence, Pioneer Challenge Foundation Academy, New York City PS 26R (The Carteret School), PS 30X (Wilton School), PS 50X (Clara Barton School), PS 96Q, PS 102X (Joseph O. Loretan), PS 104Q (The Bays Water), PS 214K (Michael Friedsam), PS 223Q (Lyndon B. Johnson School), PS 308K (Clara Cardwell), PS 333Q (Goldie Maple Academy), Sequoyah Elementary School, South Shore Charter Public School, Spartanburg Charter School, Steed Elementary School, Thomas Jefferson Classical Academy, Three Oaks Elementary, West Manor Elementary.

And a special thanks to the CKLA Pilot Coordinators Anita Henderson, Yasmin Lugo-Hernandez, and Susan Smith, whose suggestions and day-to-day support to teachers using these materials in their classrooms was critical.

CREDITS